KU-668-889

Concept of Time
What time of the day are the following activities done at

. . . .

. . . .

. . . .

. . . .

. . . .

. . . .

Assorted!
Tick the answer

The path of a planet's revolution around the sun is called

Axis   direction   plane   orbit

What colour does the earth's appear from the moon?

Green   blue   red   black

What is the milky way?

Star   planet   galaxy   satellite

What is the position of the planet earth in the solar system?

Third   sixth   fourth   second

Which planet looks red?

Pluto   mars   jupiter   mercury

DREAMLAND

KID'S
4th Activity Book

Age 6+
General Knowledge

Compiled by :
Shweta Shilpa

DREAMLAND PUBLICATIONS

J-128, Kirti Nagar, New Delhi-110 015, India
Tel. : +91-11- 2510 6050, 2543 5657
E-mail : dreamland@dreamlandpublications.com
Shop online at www.dreamlandpublications.com
Like us on www.facebook.com/DreamlandPublications

Published in 2020 by

DREAMLAND PUBLICATIONS

J-128, Kirti Nagar, New Delhi - 110 015, India
Tel. : +91-11-2510 6050, 2543 5657
E-mail : dreamland@dreamlandpublications.com
www.dreamlandpublications.com

Copyright © 2020 Dreamland Publications
All rights reserved. No part of this publication should be
reproduced, stored in a retrieval system or transmitted in any
form or by any means—electronic, mechanical, photocopying,
recording or otherwise—without the prior permission of
Dreamland Publications.
ISBN 978-81-8451-649-4

Printed in India

PREFACE

This 4th Activity Book is indeed a treasure house of fun filled moments. Every page of this book is full of entertaining assignments for children. This book on **"General Knowledge"** will enhance the child in grasping and understanding about the basic concepts of the General Knowledge.

Children will find the book interesting by involving themselves in solving mazes, adding colour to the drawings, matching the pairs, etc., and will have fun with dots and puzzles. At times, they may have to complete half-finished sketches or spot differences between pictures that almost look alike, thereby giving them a chance to think cohesively.

An attempt has been made not only to entertain but also stimulate the child's thinking, reasoning and creativity.

This book aims at providing children with a way to relax after a strenuous day of vigorous outdoor activity.

—Publisher

Safety
Colour the things red which are dangerous to play with.

Scissors

Doll

Pencil

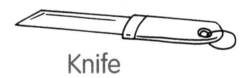

Knife

Watch

Iron

Football

Top

If I were .....
My workplacc would be .....

Teacher	Post-office
Secretary	Studio
Postman	School
Photographer	Field
Doctor	Hospital
Farmer	Office

Guess the season the picture tells

W _ _ _ _ _

A _ _ _ _ _

S _ _ _ _ _

M _ _ _ _ _ _

Eating right

BREAKFAST

Dinner rolls

Ice-Cream

Chicken

LUNCH

Cake

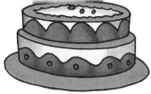

Soup

Tea

SNACKS

Cereals

Toasts

Milk

Butter

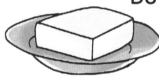

DINNER

Green Beans

Salads

Juice

Words of the day!
All animals have something to say to You!

- squeek

- quack

- sniff

- meow

- buzz

- gruff

Associate the objects to the shapes they represent.

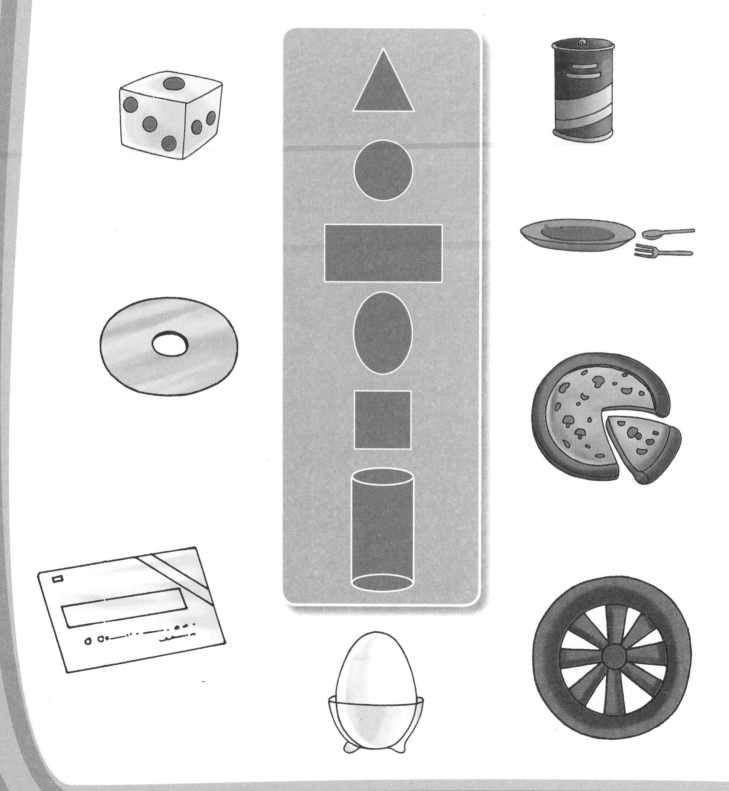

Around the world!

Begin at * and follow the moves as per directions and see where you land up.

North West-1 ☐ J
South east-1 ☐
North east-1 ☐
North west-2 ☐
West-1 ☐

North-2, East-1 ☐
South east-1 ☐
West-1 ☐
North west-2 ☐
South west-2 ☐
South east-1 ☐

N

A I Z C R
F J W P L H
W D H N * G E X E
Z O H A
D R K I

S

South-2, East-1 ☐
West-1 ☐
West-3 ☐
North-2, West-1 ☐
South east-1 ☐

North-1, West-2 ☐
North east-2 ☐
South east-1 ☐
West-1 ☐
North-2 East-1 ☐
East-2 ☐

Knowing Days

Name the days of the week.

1 [　　　] 2 [　　　] 3 [　　　]

4 [　　　] 5 [　　　] 6 [　　　]

7 [　　　]

Name the days of the week you go to school.

[　　　] [　　　] [　　　]

[　　　] [　　　]

Name the days of the week you do not go to school.

[　　　]

[　　　]

Great Masses of Land / Water

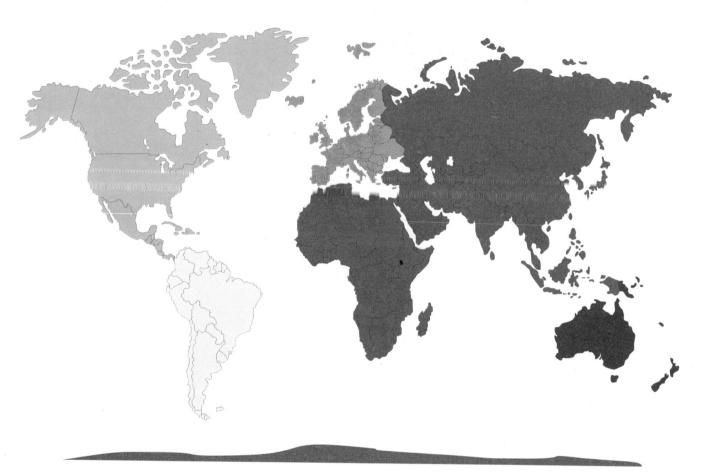

Number the following on the World-Outline Map above.

1. Asia
2. North America
3. Australia
4. Altantic Ocean
5. South America
6. Pacific Ocean
7. Africa
8. Europe
9. Aractic Ocean
10. Antarctica
11. Indian Ocean

The artists palette

purple   brown   green   orange

Mix the colours

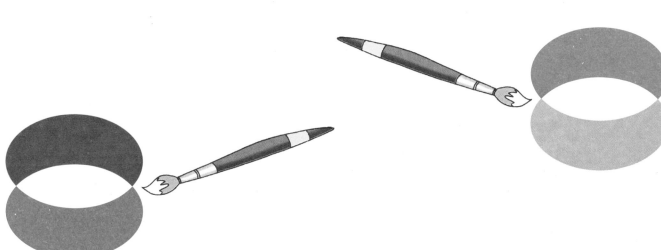

Grouping
Classify which group?

Keyboard instrument

Stringed instrument

Wind instrument

A Busy Vet!
Dr. Doolittle is curing the animals of their illness. Match the animals with the different illnesses.

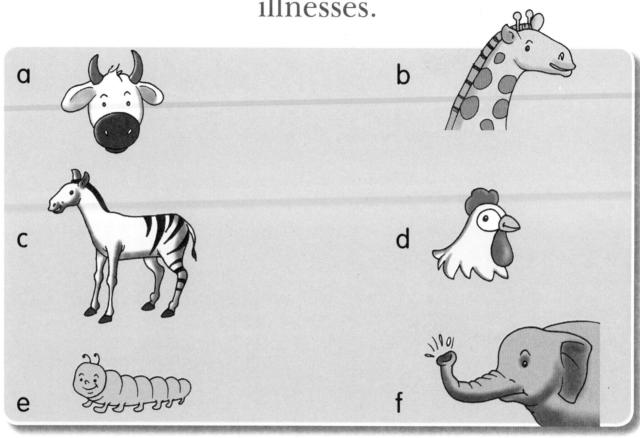

a

b

c

d

e

f

1. Chicken-pox ☐

2. Lost his stripes ☐

3. Sore feet ☐

4. Cold in the nose ☐

5. Gives "chocolate" milk ☐

6. Has no voice ☐

Spin in all directions

Expand the word below in different directions to get the four directions of planet earth.

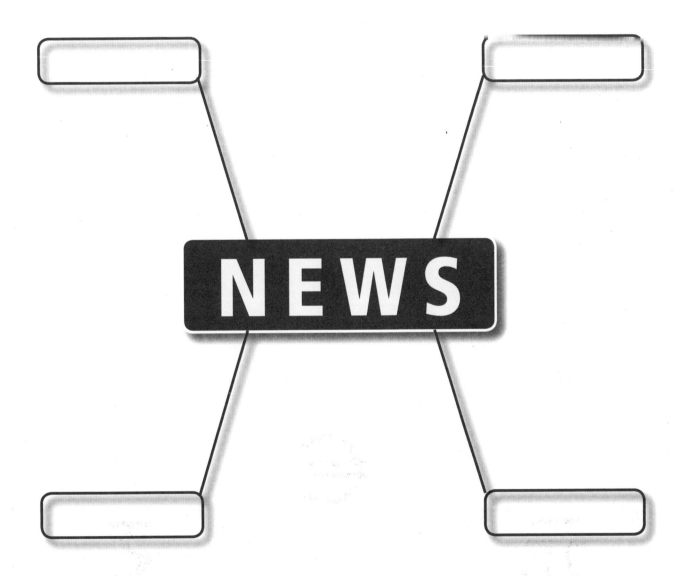

Money Talk
Know the currencies of the following countries.

Countries

China	....
Europe	....
U.S.A.	....
U.K .	....
India	....

Currency Bank

$ Dollar

£ Pound

€ Euro

元 Yuan

₹ Rupee

Bounce
Associate the sport with the type of ball it is played with...

baseball

basket-ball

tennis-ball

football

Play the Game!

The game with Jacks, Queens, Kings and Aces .....

A board game with 32 white and black squares played by 2

A game with Red Queen, and black and white counters. Played by 4 players.

A game with 16 small coins (4 coins of one colour) and can be played by 4 players max.

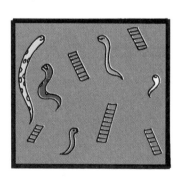

A game with snakes and ladders to move up or come down.

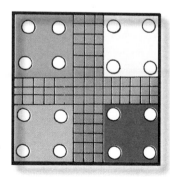

Quizzed

* Name the animal which is the logo of WWF.

☐ Eagle   ☐ Giant Panda   ☐ Bear

* Which of these is non-biodegradable

☐ Fruit-peels   ☐ Leftover food   ☐ Plastic

* Sanitary landfill is associated with

☐ Noise control   ☐ Quality control   ☐ Waste disposal

* Deafness can be caused by

☐ Air pollution   ☐ Noise pollution   ☐ Water pollution

* Which gas is both harmful and helpful to life on Earth?

☐ Ozone   ☐ Oxygen   ☐ Methane

Your Scores here.

You get 5 marks for each correct answer

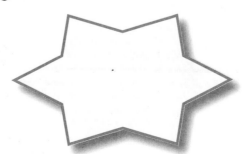

Beachside!

Traffic jam
Look for the words Car, Taxi, Bus, Plane, Train!

C	Z	P	I	T	B
A	T	X	J	R	U
R	A	S	B	A	S
T	A	O	B	I	H
R	P	L	A	N	E

Give them a colour as you keep discovering.

An Awareness Tour

Breads and cakes are made here

....

A stopping and boarding place for railway

trains ....

A place where aircrafts are kept

....

A place where meals can be eaten or bought .

....

A place where historical things are kept

....

A place where animals and birds are kept

....

Take your pick ...

Restaurant
Bakery
Museum
Zoo
Hangar
Station

Write the first letter of each picture to name a new animal

Sporty Actions

8 of the words below are sports. Figure them out and colour their frame.

football		knitting
bowling	cooking	running
swimming	volleyball	sleeping
reading	basketball	snoring
fighting	golf	wrestling

Food Path
What happens to the food I take in?

✓ Tick the statements that help the food to be digested in our body —

☐ Teeth grind the food and mix it with saliva.

☐ The skull protects the brain.

☐ From the mouth the food travels down to the stomach.

☐ The heart pumps blood around the body.

☐ From the stomach food goes through long tubes called intestines.

☐ The skeleton bones are held together by joints.

☐ The blood carries dissolved food to the liver.

Chirp-Chirp

Many birds love to live by the water side. Let fish from the water-sources. Make nests by the cliffs on the sea-side or in the grass by the pond-side. Pick in choose these water-birds from below.

Zoom by ....

Down the street go vans and lorries. Colour these in the correct colours and write their names....

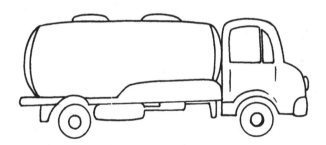

Magic Squares

Go Diagonal
or Down
or Across
and add up the rows to get the same total.

6	11	4
5	7	9
10	3	8

Numbers sum upto ....

12	5	10
7	9	11
8	13	6

Numbers sum upto ....

4	9	2
3	5	7
8	1	6

Numbers sum upto ....

10	15	5
6	11	13
14	4	12

Numbers sum upto ....

I Lost My Tail

TIGER

ELEPHANT

LION

MONKEY

HORSE

Match the tails to the animals

The Perfect Triangle

Colour the triangle with the perfect set of words. The words refer to the same category

Action Body

Actions	The Body-part that helps me...

Actions

CRY

LAUGH

SNEEZE

HAVE FRACKLES

CUTTING / BITING

BLINK

GOOSE BUMPS

PUMPING BLOOD

The Body-part that helps me...

TEETH

EYES

SKIN

NOSE

MUSCLES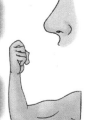

HEART

Is it (W) for Winter Clothing or
(S) for Summer Clothing.

At School

School is fun. There are so many things to learn and know. Name the ones you see below.

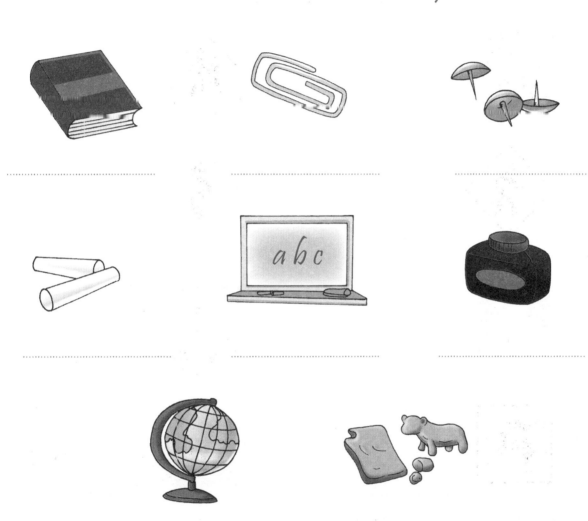

Do You Know The Signs?
Guess these signs - What do they stand for?
On the Highway.

....

....

....

....

....

....

....

....

CLUES		
AIRPORT	NARROW-BRIDGE	FOOD
PEDESTRIAN-CROSSING	SCHOOL	NO-U-TURN
CURVE AHEAD	PETROL	COURIER/ DELIVERY PERSON

Shapes
Write down the shapes of the following:

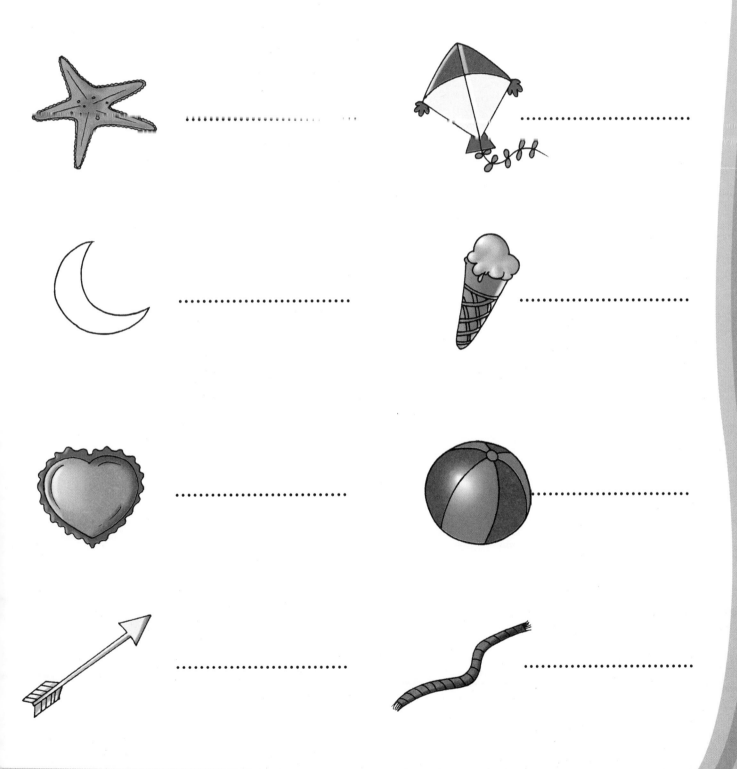

My Home
Cross-Section of a House

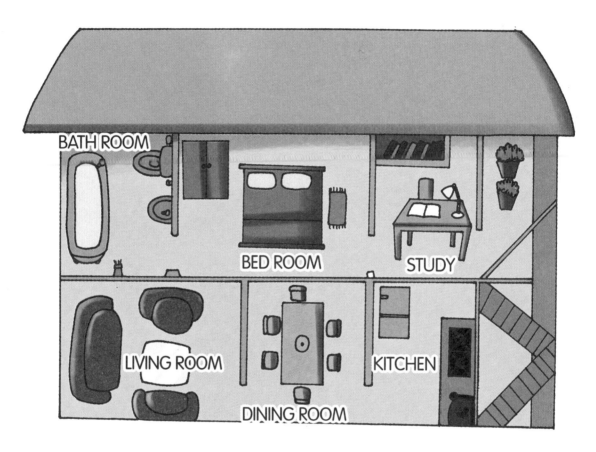

BATH ROOM

BED ROOM

STUDY

LIVING ROOM

KITCHEN

DINING ROOM

Match the given activity to the correct room :

◯ Bathe   ◯ Eat   ◯ Study

◯ Sleep   ◯ Cook   ◯ Relax

Matching
Make sets of clothes by matching.

 Shirt

 Trousers

 Coat

 Blouse/Shirt

 T-Shirt

 Tie

 Skirt

 Shorts

 Winter Cap

 Boys Swimsuit

 Girls Swimsuit

 Mufflers

I Enjoy Myself Here!
Identify these places where kids love to go .

Sea-World

Sink Or Float

What do you think will sink or float when immersed in a tub of water?

Ship

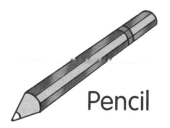

Pencil

Leaf

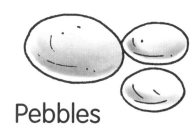

Pebbles

Oil

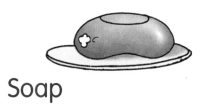

Soap

Paper

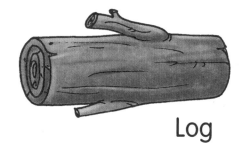

Log

Lets Move It

Connect the path from the mode of transport to the person who moves it.

Cool It

Mom just returned from the store with two big bags of grocery. As you help put things away, which one will you put in the refrigerator?

Chicken

Cauliflower

Chips

Butter

Tooth paste

Soup

Egg-tray

Cheese

Tissue box

Bulbs

Milk-pack

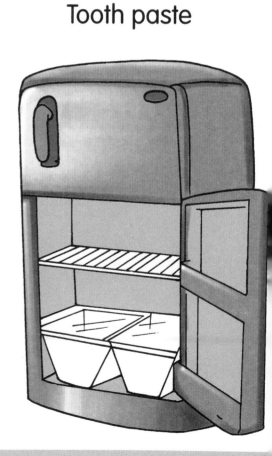

Question Mark?

What brings heat and light to our planet earth?

....

What is the source of water for lakes or other fresh water bodies?

....

What makes the moon shine?

....

What makes life on planet Earth possible.

....

Pick and Choose the Answers

Rain	The Sun	Snow Glaciers
Sunlight	Atmosphere	Water

What With What ?

Each item in the "Blue box" goes with something in the "Yellow-Box". Go Ahead! Match them .....

Blue-box

Yellow-box

Get Quizzed
Take help of picture clues to solve the crossword.

1. DOWN

I. ACROSS

¹C				²K
				D
²F			L	
	³P			

2. ACROSS

2. DOWN

3. ACROSS

Write L for Light and H for heavy.

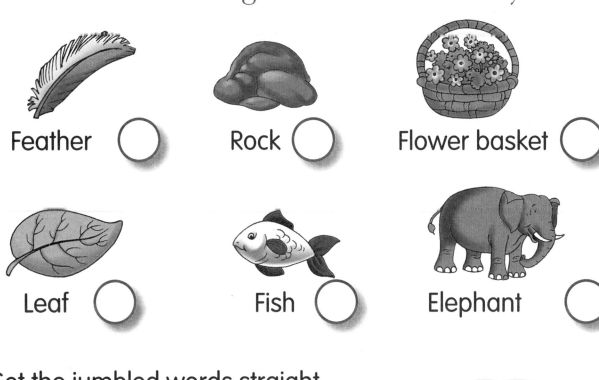

Feather ◯   Rock ◯   Flower basket ◯

Leaf ◯   Fish ◯   Elephant ◯

Get the jumbled words straight
Hint : Take off with colours

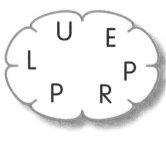

U E
L P
P R

_____

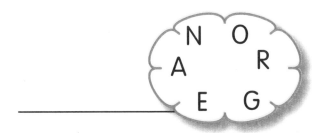

N O
A R
E G

_____

V O
T E
I L

_____

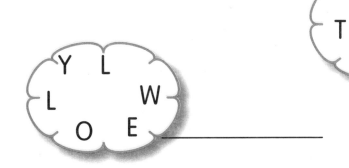

Y L
L W
O E

_____

Story Time
From the picture clues guess the story.

 A

 B

 C

 D

 E

PETER PAN   HANSEL AND GRETEL   ALADDIN

JACK AND THE BEANSTALK   CINDERELLA

Look 👀
Think 👀 and List

Under each category list one thing that begins with each letter. You need to time this to score well. Your time starts now ...

CITIES AROUND THE WORLD

T ....

M ....

B ....

V ....

N ....

FLOWERS

R ....

T ....

O ....

S ....

L ....

BREAK-FAST FOODS

P ....

T ....

M ....

C ....

F ....

Mind-Boggling

Reshuffle the letters to name a body-part.

ARE ☐ ☐ ☐

EARTH ☐ ☐ ☐ ☐ ☐

ONES ☐ ☐ ☐ ☐

Follow the directions step by step and see what you get!

In the   1st row   : Circle the first letter.

2nd row   : Circle the second letter.

3rd row   : Circle the third letter.

4th row   : Circle the fourth letter.

H	A	I	R
N	E	C	K
H	E	A	R	T
H	A	N	D

Which word you get?

○   ○   ○   ○

Hey! Help Me Find My Prop
Match each prop to the Nursery Rhyme character:

Humpty Dumpty

Old King Cole

Mary Mary Quite Contrary

Jack and Jill

Old Mother Hubbard

Mary Had A Little Lamb

Little Boy Blue

Unscramble the words to know the things one does on a Camping Trip.

A Y P L

W M I S

E H I K

T E A

B L I C M

Lead Me To ...

- the place to clean up my clothes
- a place where books are kept for reading.
- a place to get my car repaired.
- a place where dramas are staged.
- a place where photos or films are made.

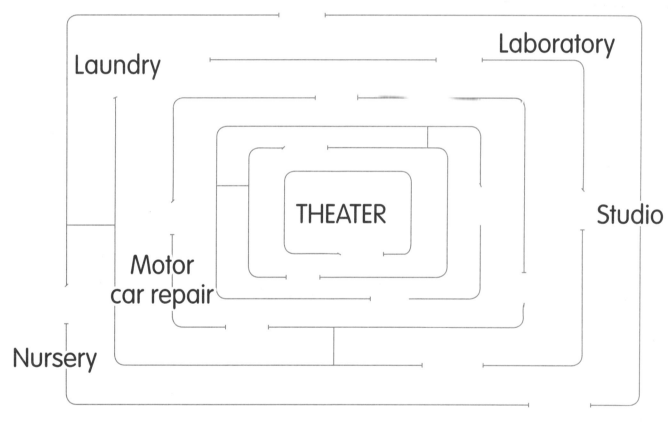

Use different coloured lines...

- a place to buy new plant saplings.
- a place where experiments are done.

Some More People Who Help Us

I make and repair wood structures ◯

I am the head cook in a restaurant/hotel and prepare the tasty food for you. ◯

I love to write books ◯

I love to act in movies, on stage or on the television ◯

I carve sculptures from various mediums such as wood, clay.... ◯

I am a ...

Colour the dots in colour pairs.

Tips : actor   chef   author   sculptor   carpenter

What Would You Do .....

- When the Signal light is showing Red.
  — Try and stop people from crossing the road.
  — Just stop my vehicle.

- When you see the symbol
  — Avoid blowing the horn.
  — Avoid the traffic signal.

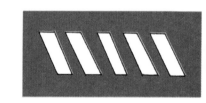

- When wanting to cross a busy road.
  — Signal the traffic to stop.
  — Look out for the Zebra Crossing.

- When walking on a busy road.
  — Use the pedestrian walk (footpath/sidewalk)
  — Walk in the middle of the road to avoid both sides traffic.

Fun with Words

Stomach Shoulder **Finger** Intestine **Chest** Ear **Hand**

Use the body-parts names to build up this pyramid.

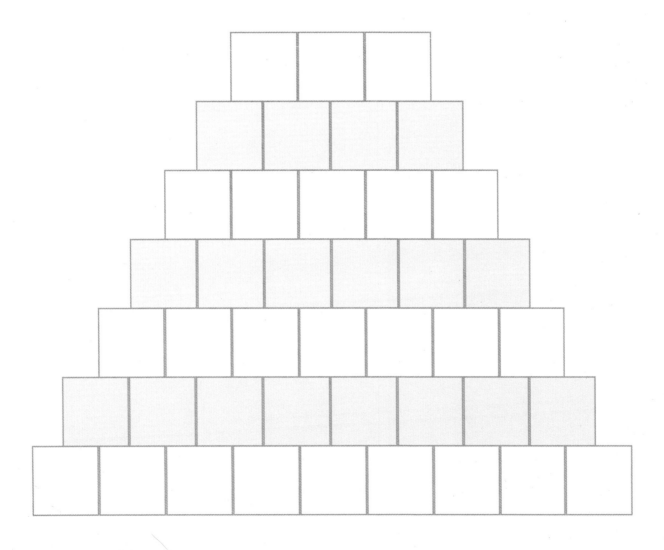

Uncode this Message

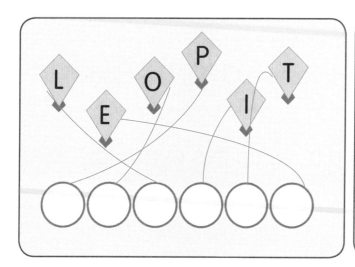

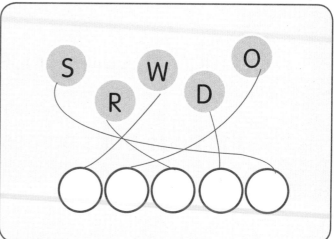

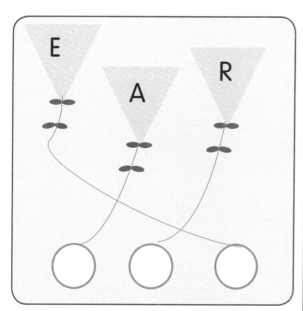

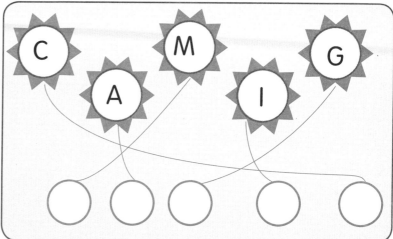

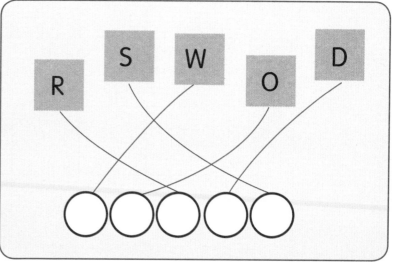

Treasure Hunt

Help the miner get to the treasure chest
and discover the jewels -

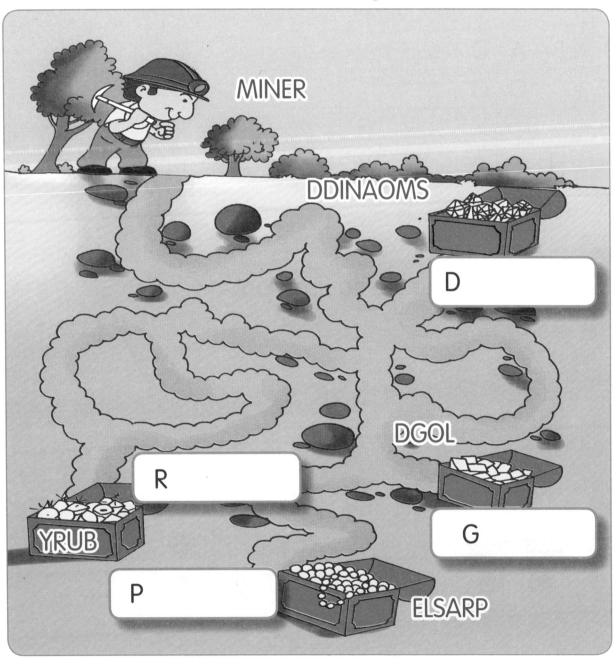

MINER

DDINAOMS

D

DGOL

R

YRUB

G

P

ELSARP

Valuable Treasures found

...................., ..., ..., ...!

Sporty Quiz

Take help of the pictures clues to identify the game in the boxes below.....

1.	B	A	D				
2.		O	O				L
3.			X		G		
4.		H			Y		
5.		R		K			

Now try identifying the equipement .....

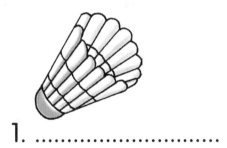

1. ....

4. ....

3. ....

2. ....

5. ....

Body Quiz
Help me name my body parts

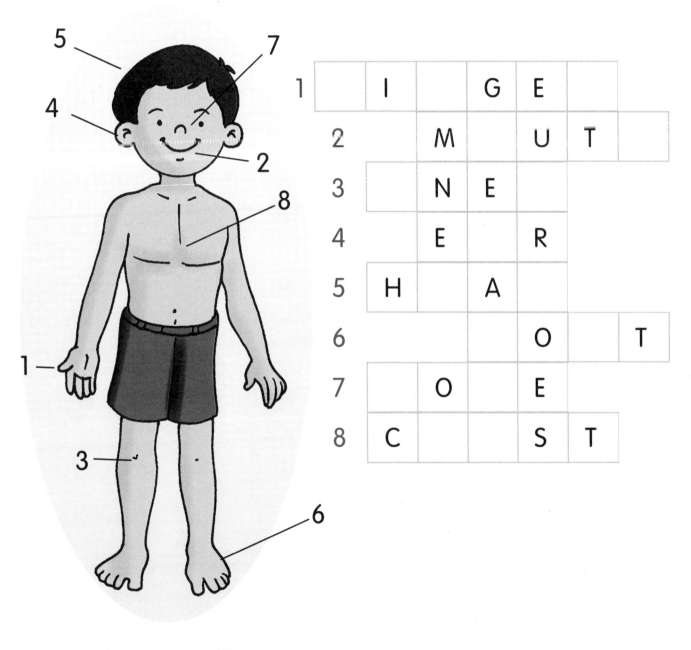

#						
1		I		G	E	
2		M		U	T	
3		N	E			
4		E		R		
5	H		A			
6				O		T
7		O		E		
8	C		S	T		

Body Quiz

Pack-up For Work
What are the things he needs to keep in his bag —

Doctor
Doctor Bag

- Thermometer ◯
- Bell ◯
- Syringe ◯
- Hammer ◯
- Sthethescope ◯
- Screwdriver ◯
- Medicines ◯

Tailor
Dress-maker

- Needle-Thread ◯
- Lamp ◯
- Bell ◯
- Inch-Tape (Measuring Tape) ◯
- Design Books ◯
- Scissors ◯

Teacher

- Books ◯
- Letters ◯
- Pen/Pencils ◯
- Chalks ◯
- Keys ◯

Adventure!
Match the adventure to the Adventure Sports by giving them the same colour ring.

A Trekker   A Scuba Diver   A Surfer

A Car Racer   Skier

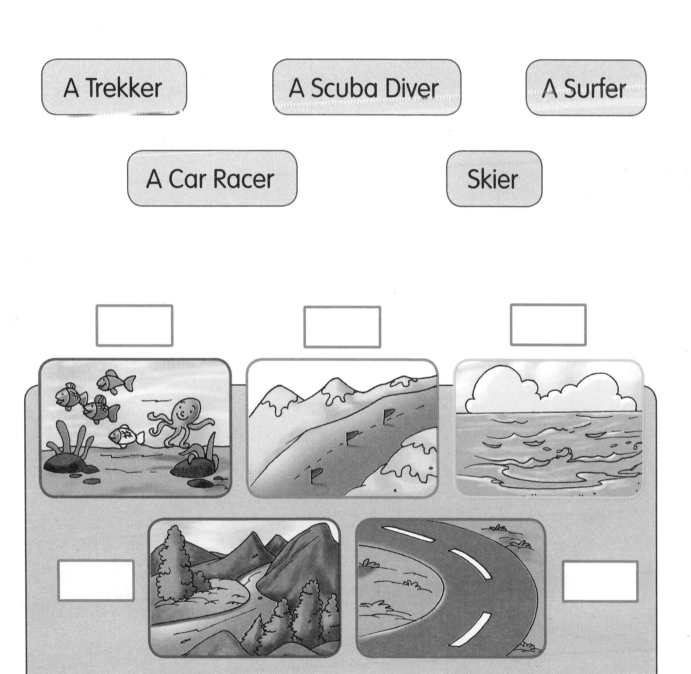

Musical Instruments

From the family of Instruments pick up the "Wind Instruments"

Tip : Wind Instruments make sound when someone blows into them.

Violin

Trumpet

Bagpiper

Harp

Bells

Drums

Flute

Mouthorgan

Saxaphone